C000271967

Kill Jill

by Mark Wheeller

Kill Jill
by Mark Wheeller

Commissioned by The Birmingham REP for The Young REP 2005.

Author's acknowledgments:
Tim Ford from from the Birmingham REP for the idea of the commission and helping me to generate some of the material for the play. Also for his ongoing enthusiasm for my work. Thanks Tim.
Birmingham Young REP for their excellent productions of the play and giving the plays a great start in life!
Evie & team from dbda who offered productive ideas for me to improve the first draft I sent them.
Sophie Gorell Barnes and all at MBA for their continued support and belief.
My wife, Rachel, and children (Ollie, Charlie & Daisy) for love and support... and tolerance of long working hours.

First edition, published by **dbda** in 2007

ISBN 9 781902 843209

BRITISH LIBRARY CATALOGUING IN PUBLICATION DATA
A catalogue record for this book is available from the British Library.

© Mark Wheeller 2007.
The moral right of the author has been asserted.

No part of this publication may be transmitted, stored in a retrieval system or reproduced in any form or by means electronic, mechanical, photocopying, typescript, recording or otherwise, without prior permission of the copyright owners.

Photocopying of scripts is illegal! Even if you hold a licence from the Copyright Licensing Agency you are only allowed to photocopy up to a total of 5% of the whole script. Please remember the writers who depend upon their share of your purchases... without them the plays which you perform could not have been written or published.

All enquiries regarding all rights associated with this play, including performing rights, should be addressed to:
Sophie Gorell Barnes, MBA Literary Agents Limited, 62 Grafton Way, London W1P 5LD.
Tel: 020 7387 2076 Fax: 020 7387 2042 E-mail: sophie@mbalit.co.uk

Further copies of this publication can be purchased from:
dbda, Pin Point, 1-2 Rosslyn Crescent, Harrow HA1 2SB.
Tel: 0870 333 7771 Fax: 0870 333 7772 E-mail: info@dbda.co.uk

I like it when my phone rings... unless it's a cold caller trying to sell something. Most times though I like it. The best times are when I'm being offered something out of the blue... something I know to be genuine. As a playwright that does happen... but only occasionally!

I'd known Tim Ford (The Artistic Director of the Birmingham Young REP group) for a few years and had become a great admirer of the award-winning productions he put on when he was working with our local *Eastleigh Borough Youth Theatre*. Two of my children (Charlie and Daisy-Lou) had been in his productions and he had directed two of my plays, **Hard To Swallow** and a highly original (and thankfully absurd!) version of **The Most Absurd Xmas Musical in the World Ever**. I was sufficiently impressed to ask him to premiere my tribute play to my friend Graham Salmon **Graham – World's Fastest Blindman** at the 2001 Edinburgh Festival. He did an amazing job on that too!

It wasn't long before his unique talent as a director was recognised and he moved to work at the Birmingham Rep! When he left he said: "one day I'll commission you to write a play for The Young REP as part of the Rep's new writers scheme". This isn't the first time someone has made this sort of suggestion... but it had never been made by someone going to work in such a prestigious Theatre. Although I was grateful, I was somewhat sceptical... I thought: I'll believe that when it actually happens!

One day in June 2004, I received a surprise phone call from Tim saying exactly that "he wanted to commission me to write a play". Yes!!!

"What do you want to write a play about?" he asked.

"I don't know." Nothing came immediately to mind, I hadn't prepared for this conversation!

"Well have a think about it and get back to me."

"What, it can be about anything?"

"Yeh."

"I'll give it some thought then."

We said our goodbyes and, as he was about to put the phone down, I said...

Introduction

"Oh, Tim there is one idea... I've wanted to do it for a while now." I went on to outline the essence of Kill Jill.

Many years before this I had witnessed Luke Abbott, who is responsible for a whole strand of my Drama teaching, doing a session based on fairy tales. I loved the way his thinking turned them upside down. This lesson got me thinking about another, *Jack and the Beanstalk*, one of my favourites. I thought it's amazing how Jack, the robber, is painted as a hero, and the victim of his crime, the poor giant, as the baddie! This needed to be addressed for the sake of that poor giant!

One day, many years later, I heard on the News that a man from Norfolk, Tony Martin, was being put in prison for shooting an intruder. I really felt for him in what seemed to be a case where he was protecting his property. In the news reports at the time the phrase "An Englishman's home should be his castle" kept cropping up and I immediately made the link between this and *Jack and the Beanstalk* (at one point *An Englishman's Home*... was a working title).

I used the idea at my school (Oaklands) with a group of Year 11's who devised a version of this upside down *Jack and the Beanstalk* story for their GCSE presentation exam. Their version, which was superb, proved that the idea had legs. The trouble was when would I get round to writing it... I already had a number of projects on the go (at that time I was doing both **Missing Dan Nolan** and **The Gate Escape**). I left it on the back burner hoping that at some stage the right opportunity would arise.

It was great to have a commission! I generally write for my own groups to perform so writing for someone else needs more care as I have to rely on them getting what I want from what I write. If I am doing it with my own groups I can change it all the time during rehearsals... and I do... making me feel that any early drafts I write must be pretty rubbish!

Kill Jill seemed to disprove my insecurity. Almost without exception Tim and his group seemed happy with the early drafts I sent. It seemed easier to write than anything I'd done before. One of the reasons for this may well have been that I had thought about it for many years and prepared, albeit in my mind, many versions of this story. However when I started putting finger to keyboard it took me by surprise. I remember Tim saying that he wanted it to be funny so I tried to write spontaneously, making wacky things happen within the general framework of the story. I also tried to make it flow from one moment to the next and not worrying about how unrealistic or forced the links were... much as I had seen Monty Python do in the early seventies... in fact, I even lifted the essence of one of their scenes (The Cheese Shop Sketch) which will ring bells for parents when they come to see this play!

I am a *Big Brother* fan so used this as an opportunity for Tim to use multimedia, which he was really keen to do. This was another bizarre twist that just happened one day and gave the story an important additional sub-theme. I remember coming up with the idea of National Service to entertainment and being particularly proud of that! It seemed to go down well in Birmingham, too. I had written it knowing that Tim would probably want a big set. Imagine my surprise when Tim said he was going to present it with barely any props or set, to show it could be done in any situation. Having said that, I think he spent thousands of pounds equipping the studio out with TV sets and cameras filming everything that happened on stage from a variety of different angles... he told me that each young camera operator had a camera script.

Our whole family went up to Birmingham to see the production. It was an amazing production and I was very proud on that occasion... three occasions in fact! I am very lucky that I see top performers and top directors performing/directing my plays. This was no exception. I loved it. It may seem arrogant to say that, but I did! I don't' think it is arrogant as I 'only' wrote it. Writing, as far as I am concerned, provides the outline. It's brilliant fun seeing how this director and young cast managed to colour it in! I approved of their 'colouring' very much! In fact, it was more like me giving them a firework rocket. It looked good enough and you could tell it had some potential, but boy when they set light to it, it really took off!!! (There is always the danger that a director or group pour water on it.) As you can tell... I loved seeing it!

There were parts I'd forgotten, parts where an individual performer impressed me, where a directorial idea impressed me and parts where I was even impressed by the writing. There were, of course, parts that I wanted to change. That happened on the train on my way home!

Introduction

I covered the script with notes to develop sections, to cut sections and to make some minor alterations! I was keen to reduce the number of characters so that the play would be appropriate for GCSE use, where my plays have become very popular.

I sent that script to my publishers, dbda, who had expressed an interest in seeing it. They liked it but came back with some really useful comments which led to the final draft that you have in this book. They thought that the balance between the comedy at the beginning and the serious at the end was slightly askew and wanted me to look at shortening the comedy.

As I read it through I realised that there was one major problem. It was the inclusion of Jack's back-story (which was the root of this whole project). It had also been a lively, popular and well-performed scene in the Birmingham Young REP production. I remembered the Connor scene in *Missing Dan Nolan* that I had really liked but could not find a place for... so I took it out and re-read the play. It made a drastic improvement in the trajectory of the story... but because (Tim and) I like the scene so much I have left it in as a "Deleted Scene"... so do have a look and try to stage it... it should get lots of laughs! You could even perform it as a prologue to this play with another group (of younger) students performing it.

What this demonstrates is that sometimes difficult and unpopular decisions have to be taken to make the whole play better. It does take courage. I remembered that it had taken a long time to perfect that scene. I certainly did not like making myself lose this scene but knew, for the play as a whole, it was for the best!

I hope that by making *Kill Jill* available, there will be groups out there willing to try to put it on and have fun with it. If you are one of those groups good luck... and please let me know through my web site (www.amdram.co.uk/wheellerplays)... if it is possible for me to come, I will try!

Mark Wheeller

11+ (3m, 3f , 5+ m or f)

Jill Wentup	
Becky Wentup	Jill's mum. (In the first production this role was played by a male actor as a pantomime dame. It added substantially to the comedy and I thoroughly approve of this idea!)
John Wentup	Jill's dad
Isabel	A temptress.
George Jhiyonne	He who lives at the top of the beanstalk.
PC Plodder	
Cindy	Jill's friend
Jack MacBeanstalk	Jill's new boyfriend
*Assistants 1 & 2	Shop assistants
*Camera Operator	

* There can be more Camera Operators and Assistants if you need them.

For **GCSE extracts** two distinct extracts can be done of this play:
The first half, **Sections 1-6** can be done by a **cast of 5**. It could be preceded by a version of the "deleted scene" should you be concerned that the candidates do not have enough to do!
Section 7 can be performed as a stand-alone section by a **cast of 5**: *2m/2f & 1m or f* (15 – 20 minute running time). It could also be preceded by a version of the "deleted scene".

Cast list for the 5 player version:

2m, 2f, 1m or f with doubling

Actor 1: (Female)	Jill
Actor 2: (Female)	Isabel; Cindy; Camera Operator
Actor 3: (Female or Male)	Becky; Assistant 2
Actor 4: (Male)	PC Plodder; Jack
Actor 5: (Male)	John; George; Assistant 1

Foreword by Tim Ford, Director, The Young REP

I have been a friend of Mark's and an admirer of his plays for a very long time and I have always wanted to be in a position to be able to commission him to write a play for me. In 2004 I was fortunate enough to be given the job of Artistic Director of The Young REP (The Birmingham REP's Youth Theatre) based at The REP and here I found my opportunity to commission him. I have always liked the way his plays play with audiences and allow ample opportunities for young performers to shine. So in June 2004 I called him up and the commission commenced.

The play began its life as a simple phone call to Mark and me popping the question to him (to write the play not marriage that is!) and I was delighted when he agreed to give it a go. My brief to him was very clear; I wanted a play for a cast of approximately 24 young people with plenty of parts for everyone. I also wanted him to really challenge himself and write something different and something that was FUNNY! Mark has never seen himself as someone that writes funny so I knew that there in would lie the greatest challenge of them all for him. I also asked Mark knowing his great knowledge of theatre technology (which is very limited I can tell you!) to write a play that used loads of what I call toys and gadgets e.g. video cameras, projectors, laptops etc... I had used live cameras in performance before and had a great deal of fun and success in turning them on the audience and I was sure that this was an element of the play that I wanted Mark to explore further. It also felt right at the time with the whole *Big Brother* thing happening. I thought that it was an avenue that needed exploring and was something that would be interesting for us to see what would happen if we took reality television to the extreme. How far are we prepared to go for entertainment? So very slowly we were having the makings of a classic Mark Wheeller play. A Youth Theatre friendly play with a message! A fairly simple brief all in all I thought.

Now, knowing Mark, I knew that he would write a great play and that, as he had always enjoyed writing fairy tales and playing around with fairy story characters (not in his garden though), I would be in for a treat. I was also preparing myself for the famous Wheeller twist in the story and I was not disappointed. So 'Kill Jill' was born.

We had regular phone calls to each other over the initial first few weeks as he would test ideas out on me and then I would, in turn, take them back to my group and then phone Mark – or rather he would be calling me the second the session had finished to get the news on how it had gone. He was always so nervous and so excited at the end of the phone, like a little sweet school child again. I remember one phone call going something like: "So how did the cow section go and what did they think of the mask?", "The writing was great but the rubber mask was hot!" I even remember the two us reading the play through over the phone to each other scene by scene with us playing ALL the characters fully, voices and all! So the insanity continued, as did the play. The group loved it; I can't remember having so much silly fun in a rehearsal room for ages. From the crazy Monty pythonesque shopkeepers to the mad northern Cindy and the insane high-speed storytellers, it was all great. The play provided us with many new catch phrases and the young people loved it. Moo yak a sha! Oh my days! We had so much fun each week devising and trying the script out that Mark had sent to us, never knowing where it would go next. We loved Mark's clever twist on the traditional nursery rhyme characters and the way he had woven them together. Everybody was kept busy I was pleased to say, not a single spear-carrier in sight (not that there is anything wrong with spear carriers of course).

As far as staging the play goes, I knew that Mark was expecting me to give it the full works, a huge set, the all singing all dancing lighting and the wonderfully detailed costumes and props that he was so very used to seeing from my productions. Well, I thought I would actually go the other way and try and stage it as simply as I possibly could. I knew that if it could be staged with the bare minimum of set and props and I could still make it work and look great, that it would be a play that many schools and youth groups would be interested in doing. I know how budget, or lack of it, is always a problem for many groups.

For the original production we used a huge piece of artificial grass that was attached to the grid and came down the back of the theatre and across the floor area. This made the piece feel very outdoors and bright and then, with very simple lighting effects (gobos), we were able to make the grass look like the beanstalk, the hill, the kitchen and the shop. I placed the camera operators on the corners of the grass with the sound operators and then hung lots of televisions above the acting space for the audience to watch the action. The televisions all had live feeds to each of the cameras and this really was the making of the show as we were able to get some fantastic close up shots from all angels at all times, even if it did make the actors feel very exposed. If you do nothing with the set you must! Must! Must! get yourself a load of televisions and cameras, they made a huge difference to the play. We used a whole range of cameras, from very cheap security cameras to top of the range video cameras. We

Foreword

also used two doorframes that became invaluable as the play went on. The frames were used for all the character entrances and doubled up, with a cloth over them, as the table and shop counter; they were also used for a well and a mirror.

Another little thing I was keen on doing with the play, was to play around with the casting and gender. I have always loved Monty Python and the play was full of little Python moments and so it felt perfectly natural to cast the role of the mum (Becky) as a boy in the style of Brian's mum in "The Life of Brian". It worked so well and really brought the comedy out of the text and gave the scenes with Jill real energy. I can still here him/her swearing out loudly in the quander scene and the impact it had on the audience, everybody was in stitches. To see a young lad dressed, as Nora Batty speaking/yelling in a high pitch voice is something you never forget. So please be brave in your casting and play around with gender.

The play was performed in November of 2005 in The Door studio theatre at The Birmingham REP and I am pleased to say was a great success, the show sold out and everybody loved it and more importantly they laughed. Yes, Mark Wheeller had written a very funny play. We had loads of fun with the cameras too, and the ending came as a great surprise to everybody. We had hit onto a real winner. I was delighted with the play and feel a great sense of pride to have been part of this new piece. I can only hope that you all have as much fun as we did, both reading it and performing it. It is a very challenging piece with lots of lovely cameo roles; it allows the cast to devise small sections such as the opening sequence but it also demands respect for the text during the final tense section. *Kill Jill* combines both comedy and tragedy and is a play that will challenge all abilities of actors and directors. It is a very full text but it really works and yes, it's really funny! So what are you waiting for? Big Brother is watching you! Moo yak a sha!

Tim Ford

Director, The Young REP

December 2006

Kill Jill was first performed by The Young REP at
The Birmingham Repertory Theatre in October 2005.

Director:	Tim Ford
Designer:	Tim Ford
Producer:	The Birmingham REP

Original Cast:

Jill:	Nicola Ali
Becky:	Chris Todd
Police:	Hannah Edwards
George:	Jerry Orme
Cindy:	Katherine Allen
Jack:	Scott Crupmton
Jeweller:	Sean Cunoosamy
Shop Assistant:	Ian Farnell
Shop Assistant:	Dore Robinson
Story Teller:	Tom Wright
Story Teller:	Nick Abbey
Story Teller:	Annabel Betts
Story Teller:	Oliver Jones
Story Teller:	Helen Yates
Camera Operator 1:	Rosie Adams
Camera Operator 2:	Jodie Melbourne
Camera Operator 3:	Eliza Harris
Camera Operator 4:	Lauren Dyson
(Sound Operator 1):	Joseph Turner
(Sound Operator 2):	Sade Hussain Williams
(Sound Operator 3):	Chad Furhuraire
(Sound Operator 4):	Stephen Turner

Photographs from The Young REP production

Photographs by Dijana Capan

Chapter 1:   Birth of First 'Reality' Death Star

(Before the production begins cameras sited on or around the stage should be looking out to the audience and showing live on screen various moments as the audience enter etc. There should be appropriate close ups of individuals in the audience wherever possible. On a given cue, a voice over booms out. The audience continue to be shown on screen(s) during the speech.

Voice Over: Ladies and Gentlemen. Welcome to The Lottery Reality Show! The show that can strike anyone, anywhere at any time!
Tonight, The Lottery Reality Show has chosen this theatre to provide us with the new candidate for this month's programme.

(The camera focuses on a section of the audience that includes Jill. Use any opportunity to 'tease' members of the audience with close ups, etc. throughout the following speech.)

We can already see the person that will become the face of this time in history. A bold claim... but one we're confident to make.

(The camera closes in gradually on Jill.) Ladies and gentlemen, this month we have a fourteen year old who has the opportunity to entertain the whole of Ganderland with her life.

(Jill is now the only audience member in shot.)

Jill: Shit!

Voice Over: Please do not swear.

Jill: Sorry... I'm just a bit shocked!

Voice Over: The Lottery Reality Show is proud to present... Jill Wentup.

Jill: What do I do now?

Voice Over: You'll have to speak up.

Jill: *(Standing)* What do you want me to do now?

Voice Over: For one month, your life is our entertainment!

Jill: So just act normally? This isn't a joke, is it?

Chapter 1

Voice Over:	No, this is The Reality Lottery Show.
Jill:	Are you gonna show my background like they did with that minger last time?
Voice Over:	You know your stuff Miss Wentup. Now get yourself on stage. So, ladies and gentlemen, through the magic of The Lottery Reality Show we bring you: Jill Wentup's back story!

Music: Green Hornet by Al Hirt from the Kill Bill soundtrack* *plays to denote that the play is to begin. Each Chapter and its title should be projected onto a screen at the back of the stage. The opening sequence is performed as a melodrama either live under a strobe or previously filmed and projected onto a screen. The events should be performed with as much comedy as possible and should be in the following order.*

1/ John meets Becky. There is some flirting until they fall in love.

2/ Becky falls pregnant!

3/ A stork delivers a baby girl (Jill). They are happily surprised.

4/ 14 Years later.

5/ It is established that they are a happy family. John is very much in love with Becky and, if either Becky or Jill encounter danger, John appears like a hero to rescue them.

6/ Isabel enters appearing as a seductress with a cape. She watches them. Jill and Becky do not notice John being distracted by her.

7/ John goes towards her. He freezes, looking at Isabel.

---

* The suggested music is not covered by any of the performing rights associated with this play. Separate applications to the appropriate bodies will need to be made for public performances.

8/ Isabel approaches John… taps him on the shoulder. Initially he resists her temptation but finally he becomes emotionally and physically entwined with Isabel. He shows he is enjoying the relationship and, with Becky and Jill still otherwise occupied, he walks off with Isabel. Isabel laughs an evil laugh.

Chapter 2:   No Tea Bags!

Music: *The Grand Duel* by Luis Bacalov from the *Kill Bill* soundtrack *underscores the following scene amplifying the increasingly melancholy/ melodramatic mood.*

A team of (on stage) camera operators continues to film the following scenes. A table and three chairs are brought onto the stage with a large card or letter saying GONE in big letters. Becky enters and sees the letter/card. She reads it and slowly moves to sit by the table, head in hands, crying.

Jill enters.

Jill:	Mum? What's the matter? *(She puts her arm round Becky.)*
Becky:	Don't love… you'll make me cry even more.
Jill:	Is it dad?
Becky:	Yeh.
Jill:	He's gone? *(Becky holds up the card saying GONE)* For good? *(She turns the card round. It says FOR GOOD. Becky cries loudly.)* We'll be ok mum.
Becky:	I don't know what we're gonna do.
Jill:	What do you mean?
Becky:	How'll we cope?
Jill:	We will, mum. Don't worry.
Becky:	*(Angrily)* It's easy for you to say that.
Jill:	I didn't mean to be…
Becky:	I know… it's just…
Jill:	Do you want me to get you a cup of tea?
Becky:	*(Melodramatically allowing her pent up emotions to come out)* Jill! We can't even afford tea bags! *(Pause, then very slowly)* I only have one quander left.

Jill:	*(Brightly)* I've got one. Two should be enough. I'll pop and get some?
Becky:	This isn't how your opening scene should be... me crying... everything going wrong like this.
Jill:	So, we've got to do something.
Becky:	Like what?
Jill:	Show grit and determination?
Becky:	How?
Jill:	Take each other's hands.
Becky:	Look up to the heavens.
Both:	And vow to overcome whatever problems are put before us.
Becky:	No... that's kak!
Jill:	You suggest something then?
Becky:	Wreak revenge on Dad's new girlfriend. *(Isabel, unseen by Becky and Jill enters wearing a straw hat and other suitable holiday garments and walks across the stage seductively)*
Jill:	Mum!
Becky:	No, we can't afford to go wherever they've gone!
Jill:	Mum? Do I have to do this?
Becky:	What?
Jill:	This Lottery Reality Show thing?
Becky:	Of course!
Jill:	Why?
Becky:	It's your duty.
Jill:	Duty?
Becky:	To entertain.
Jill:	Why me?

Chapter 2

Becky:	It could have been anyone… and will be next month. Anyway, I thought you wanted to be famous.
Jill:	Not like this.
Becky:	You've got to think of other people's entertainment Jill.
Jill:	It would've been alright last year when we were happy?
Becky:	Not much entertainment in a happy family, is there?
Jill:	Suppose not.
Becky:	But there will be if you can turn things around and become happy.
Jill:	Yeh! You could find a rich boyfriend!
Becky:	I can't… I…
Jill:	Don't go making excuses…
Becky:	Well. if it's that easy you go and do it!
Jill:	Alright. I will.
Becky:	Seriously.
Jill:	I like a challenge.
Becky:	What about my tea bags?
Jill:	I'm on a mission! You get them! *(Hands Becky a coin and exits with determination!)*

Chapter 3:   A Crime Reported

(The cameras all leave the stage… or turn away and stop filming.
George and the police are facing away from each other, giving the illusion of distance. They are speaking together on the phone.)

PC Plodder: We'll send someone round right away.

George: You say that every time, PC Plodder!

PC Plodder: Someone will be round in a very short while.

George: Short while! I was robbed last Tuesday and it took your fellows till Wednesday to get here. It ain't good enough. An Englishman's house should be his castle!

PC Plodder: If you'd like to make an official complaint Mr…

George: I just want you to get these little scrotes!

PC Plodder: We're doing as much as we can, but we have very little to go on.

George: The only way you'll get 'em is to have one of your boys stay round here…

PC Plodder: We can't do that Mr Jhiyonne… we do have other crimes in the area to consider.

George: I've been robbed four times in four weeks… four times!!! And you lot do nothing, just stand back and watch it happening! If you ain't gonna catch 'em, you don't leave me no choice. I'll do it mysen' *(sic)*!

PC Plodder: I advise you to leave that to us. We're trying our best and we will get them.

George: You're a joke you lot!

PC Plodder: I know you're not happy…

George: If I had my way I'd…

PC Plodder: Mr Jhiyonne, please calm down, it doesn't help matters…

George: If I had my way I'd…

Chapter 3

George & All:	*(Everyone pops on stage for a moment.)* Tie them all up against a wall and shoot the lot of them!
PC Plodder:	I know Mr Jhiyonne. You've said before but you mustn't take the law into your own hands… that's a crime, too… just leave it to us.
George:	I mean it… mark my words… I bloody mean it this time! If some bugger dares to cross my threshold I'll have him mysen'. You lot just lets 'em get away with it. It ain't right… you got to do summat… and if you lot won't, then I shall… you just wait and see! *(He slams the phone down.)* Little scrotes!

Chapter 4: Jill's Big Challenge!

Cindy:	*(All cameras re-enter and start filming again. Cindy enters carrying a box.)* Oh my days, Jill!
Jill:	Cindy?
Cindy:	My best mate a TV celebrity! My mum's watching on the internet! Wicked, innit?
Jill:	Not for me! You can leave when you want. I'm trapped on it for a month!
Cindy:	I wish they'd chosen me.
Jill:	So do I! Anyway I'm on a mission…
Cindy:	I know! To get a rich boyfriend!
Jill:	I forgot you've been watching me talk to mum….
Cindy:	I've watched it all and I've got an idea. What about Jack?
Jill:	Jack? *(Jack's picture appears on the screen.)*
Cindy:	Jack MacBeanstalk.
Jill:	He ain't rich!
Cindy:	He is! Bling not ming!
Jill:	But I actually do like him. It'd be so embarrassing if he says no.
Cindy:	*(Laughing)* As if!
Jill:	How am I gonna… you know… get him to… you know…?
Cindy:	Easy!
Jill:	Yeh?
Cindy:	Look. *(She opens the box.)*
Jill:	A cow mask?
Cindy:	Yeh.
Jill:	Don't get it!

Chapter 4

Cindy:	Oh my days, Jill! Put it on!
Jill:	What?
Cindy:	Put it on!
Jill:	Why?
Cindy:	It'll make him laugh!
Jill:	You're mad!
Cindy:	If he thinks you've got a sense of humour… he'll… well you know…
Jill:	Yeh, but…
Cindy:	Put it on!
Jill:	No!
Cindy:	Alright then… *(Starts to close the box.)* Your choice. But if you don't I can't help you. *(She turns to leave.)* See you mate.
Jill:	Cindy?
Cindy:	*(Turning)* Yeh.
Jill:	I'll try it.
Cindy:	*(Very excited)* I knew you would! *(She gets the cow mask out of the box.)* Face away from me. I want it to be a surprise!
Jill:	*(Facing away from the audience, she puts the mask on.)* It's a bit awkward.
Cindy:	When you turn round… do it real seductively!
Jill:	No way!
Cindy:	Go on! Let me count you down. *(As she counts, Jack enters with lots of bling.)* Three… two… one. *(Jill turns seductively to face Jack and Cindy.)*
Jack:	*(Laughing)* What's going on here then? Is this all for the cameras?
Cindy:	No Jack. Jill was wearing this especially for you!

Jill:	*(Ripping the mask off.)* Cindy!
Jack:	You remind me of my… my Buttercup!
Cindy:	I thought you sold her!
Jack:	Yeh, but I had to! *(He breaks down.)*
Jill:	Hey Jack… don't get upset.
Jack:	She wasn't just… she was…
Jill:	I know…
Jack:	You don't though.
Jill:	It's all coming out wrong… what I meant was…
Jack:	What?
Jill:	Jack, I want to…
Jack:	Jill… is it true what you said on the telly?
Jill:	What?
Jack:	That you… you know…
Jill:	No.
Jack:	You want to go out with me?
Jill:	This is weird!
Jack:	Cos I've… well, I've always really fancied you and didn't think you liked me!
Jill:	Well…
Cindy:	Hey you two… I think I'm in the way here… so… shall I just… you know… go?
Jill:	*(Running over to Cindy and taking her by the hand.)* Thanks Cind. I couldn't have done this without you.
Cindy	No problem. That's what friends are for! I'll be watching it live to see what happens. Be careful. *(They kiss.)* See ya. *(Cindy exits.)*
Jill:	Did you hear everything I said to Cindy before?

Jack: Yeh... that's why I came...

Jill: It isn't only the money... honest.

Jack: I know.

Jill: But the money is important. My dad's left Ganderland. We need quanders!

Jack: I know! Here! *(He brings out a wad of notes and puts it in her hands.)* There's plenty more where that came from.

Jill: What do you mean?

Jack: You'll find out one day but for now, go and tell your mum you've completed your mission and me... I'll be getting more of this! *(Waves the wad!)* Hey... watch out! Scene change!
(A table and chair is brought on.)

Jill: Wow!

Jack & Jill: Here comes my/your kitchen!

Voice Over: — I've been asked to inform you that if any rude, or indeed very rude words, are used by any of our characters, a warning sign will appear so that the more sensitive among you can avert your ears at the appropriate moment.
(Silence. Then to the characters on stage)
Right... I've finished. Carry on!

Chapter 5:   Quanders, Quanders, Quanders!

Jill:	*(Becky is sitting at the table. She shows through-out this scene her dislike of the camera operators.)* Mum?
Becky:	Where have you been?
Jill:	Weren't you watching?
Becky:	I was getting the teabags!
Jill:	Was two quanders enough?
Becky:	Yes... but now we haven't got any left!
Jill:	Wrong!
Becky:	What do you mean?
Jill:	*(Jill shows Becky her wad of notes)* Look! *(A warning is shown on screen or handheld sign: WARNING - SWEAR WORD. Jill pulls out the wad.)*
Becky:	Fucking hell Jill!
Jill:	Mum!
Becky:	Where did you get that from?
Jill:	Jack MacBeanstalk.
Becky:	Jack Mac Beanstalk? Where did he get it from? His family's even poorer than us!
Jill:	Not now they're not.
Becky:	I hope it's not too dodgy.
Jill:	What if it is?
Becky:	Jill?
Jill:	Mum you're so... I don't know... it's just this'll buy us teabags and... well whatever we want!
Becky:	What's in that box?
Jill:	Nothing.
Becky:	What do you mean, nothing?
Jill:	You wouldn't be interested.
Becky:	I am.

Chapter 5

Jill:	I'm not showing you…
Becky:	Why the big secret?
Jill:	No reason.
Becky:	So what is it?
Jill:	A mask.
Becky:	*(Silence)* A what?
Jill:	A mask.
Becky:	What do you want a mask for?
Jill:	I don't.
Becky:	So why have you got one?
Jill:	You wouldn't understand.
Becky:	Try me?
Jill:	Cindy thought it would be a good idea if I wore the mask to help me complete my mission… you should be grateful.
Becky:	It sounds a bit perverted!
Jill:	*(Getting the mask out and putting it on.)* Actually Mum it's not… it's a cow mask!
Becky:	I can feel a swear word coming on! Do I really want to know how wearing a cow mask helped my daughter to 'pull' Jack MacBeanstalk? No! Jill you worry me!
Jill:	*(Taking the mask off and handing her the wad.)* Just take this and do some retail therapy. Go fill those cupboards mother!
Becky:	What're you going to do?
Jill:	Develop my relationship with Jack. *(She exits.)*
Becky:	Jill, you be careful!
Jill:	*(Shouting to instruct the stage hands.)* Scene change! *(Becky is lifted off stage kicking and screaming by the stage hands.)*

Chapter 6: Jack and Jill's Relationship Develops!

Jack:	Look! *(He holds out a wad of notes!)*
Jill:	Where're you getting all this from?
Jack:	*(Jack taps his nose)* Come on, let's go!
Jill:	Where?
Jack:	Up the hill!
Jill:	The hill?
Jack:	Yeh, there's this well up there, and the water is like… you've gotta try it!
Jill:	Ok then, but first I want to go to the crown shop.
Jack:	The what?
Jack & Jill:	*(Indicating)* The crown shop.
Jack:	*(Two shop Assistants, who need to be grossly overplayed, enter bringing on with them, a counter with one crown on it.)* Strange! I'd never noticed that before!
Jill:	Wait outside. I want this to be a surprise.
Jack:	Mmm? What can you be getting from a crown shop? Hey, let me do the sound effect as you go in through the door.
Jill:	Cool!
Jack:	Ding-ding!
Assistants1&2:	Good afternoon madam.
Jill:	Hi. Do you have a crown for my boyfriend?
Assistant 1:	This is a crown shop.
Jill:	One with diamonds on it.
Assistant 1:	Diamonds?
Assistant 2:	No…
Assistant 1:	Sorry…
Assistant 2:	None of those I'm afraid

Chapter 6

Assistants 1 & 2:	… Madam.
Jill:	What about one with little pointy bits at the top.
Assistant 2:	Not at mid day…
Assistants 1 & 2:	… Madam.
Jill:	What about a golden one with a place for a photograph at the front.
Assistant 2:	Normally Madam, yes…
Assistant 1:	… but today the delivery man has a very nasty bug…
Assistants 1 & 2:	… Madam.
Jill:	Not much of a crown shop, is it?
Assistant 1 & 2:	*(Furious)* This is the finest Crown Shop in Ganderland!
Jill:	The only one!
Assistant 1:	How about this? *(He lifts up the only crown on the counter.)*
Assistant 2:	A wondrous item Madam.
Jill:	With Rice Krispies on it!
Assistants 1 & 2:	And… it's made out of plastic!
Assistant 1:	Pure plastic.
Jill & Assistants 1 & 2:	Fantastic!
Assistants 1 & 2:	Four hundred quanders.
Jill:	Deal! *(She hands the Assistant a wad of notes and goes to leave.)*
Assistants 1 & 2:	Wait!
Jill:	What?
Assistant 1:	We have more to say!
Assistants 1 & 2:	Young people like you make us so angry!

Assistant 1:	*(Speaking fast)* This cost five quanders to make!
Assistant 2:	You paid four hundred quanders…
Assistant 2:	… for a crown made out of brittle plastic…
Assistant 1:	… which could break at any moment…
Assistant 2:	… and its decorations are mere breakfast cereal!
Assistant 1 & 2:	Have you no sense of values?
Jill:	I bought this as a romantic gesture for my boyfriend… and you've belittled my efforts. How dare you treat your customers like this!
Assistant 1:	It's just that…
Assistant 1 & 2:	… we were about to put it in the window!
Jill:	Get another one!
Assistant 1 & 2:	We don't have any others!
Jill:	And you call this a crown shop?
Assistant 1:	Yes!
Assistant 2:	It's the best in Ganderland!
Assistant 1:	But after considerable reflection on your comments…
Assistant 2:	… only made a moment ago…
Assistant 1:	We will change!
Assistant 2:	Yes, we will!
Assistant 1:	From now on… we…
Assistant 1 & 2:	… will sell bandages!
Jill:	Bandages?
Assistant 2:	Never know when you might need a bandage, do you?
Jill:	*(As she leaves the shop.)* What are you talking about?

Chapter 6

Jack:	*(As Jill opens the door.)* Ding-ding. *(The Assistant slides the counter off stage. Jill moves towards Jack.)*
Jill:	Close your eyes and open your hands. *(He does so. Jill places the plastic crown in his hands.)* You can open them now.
Jack:	A crown! Can I put it on?
Jill:	Course!
Jack:	I feel like a king.
Jill:	You're my King. *(They come together to kiss. Jill pulls away.)* I want to… but… not with the cameras.
Jack:	After they've gone?
Jill:	There'll be no stopping me.
Jack:	Promises, promises.
Jill:	This is probably the best thing that's ever happened to me!
Jack:	And me! *(They laugh.)* Come on then… I'll race you… to the top of the hill. *(In the original Birmingham Rep production Jack and Jill end up at the top of a small step ladder placed on stage during their journey.)*
Jill:	Alright… but be careful… don't want any accidents do we?
Jack:	Run.
Jill:	Puff!
Jack:	Run.
Jill:	Puff!
Jack & Jill:	Pant… pant… pant! *(Pointing to the Camera Operator(s).)*
Jack:	I'm really thirsty. *(Some of the cast/camera operators? create 'body-scenery' of a well. They conceal a bucket in the middle of them.)*

Jill:	Look! The well!
Jack:	I'll fetch a pail of water. You won't believe how wicked it is!
Jill:	I'll do it; I don't want you having any accidents.
Jack:	Don't be silly!
Jill:	Stay there. It's no trouble, Jack. *(Jill looks into the well, loses her balance and falls in.)*
Jack:	*(Runs to help her. As he does so the 'well' runs off)* Jill!
Jill:	Want a drink? *(She passes the bucket to Jack.)*
Jack:	Are you ok?
Jill:	Course I am.
Jack:	But you've just fallen down a well.
Jill:	This place is well weird!
Jack:	Jill… sorry but I can't stay any longer!
Jill:	Is it too weird for you then… weirrrd?
Jack:	No… I've got to get back.
Jill:	We've only just arrived!
Jack:	I know, but we've got what we came for and…
Jill:	And what?
Jack:	I have to get more Quanders.
Jill:	Where from?
Jack:	I can't explain. I'm meeting Wolfey?
Jill:	Wolfey?
Jack:	Do you know him?
Jill:	Yeh, wasn't his grandma murdered in some gangland thing?
Jack:	You'd believe anything! She was actually speared

to death by a pack of wild Unicorns.

Jill:	He's bad news!
Jack:	*(Looks at watch.)* Oh no! I'm meant to meet him in fifteen minutes. Come on! *(Jack runs off stage. There is a clatter off stage as though he has 'tumbled down'.)*
Jill:	*(Running after him)* Jack! *(They both re-enter. Jack has blood on his head. Jill has her arm round him and is holding his crown.)* At least you didn't break your crown…
Jack:	*(Holding the crown of his head.)* Oh yes I have!
Jill:	*(She takes the plastic crown from him)* I mean this one.
Jack:	It really hurts. Look at all this blood!
Jill:	I know just the place for you! Look!

(Assistants 1 & 2 enter wearing an assortment of bandages and bringing on a counter.)

Jack:	The crown shop?
Jill:	No!
Assistants & Jill:	Bandage shop.
Jack:	I want a fish and chip shop!
Jill:	What?
Assistant 1	You won't find…
Assistants 1 & 2:	… bandages…
Assistant 2:	… in a…
Assistant 1:	… fish…
Assistant 2:	…and…
Assistant 1:	… chip…
Assistants 1 & 2:	… shop.

Jack:	I need vinegar and brown paper to heal my crown!
Jill:	Vinegar and brown paper?
Jack:	It's what I have to do… the rhyme.
Jill:	What?
Jack:	Up got Jack and home did trot As fast as he could caper. He went to bed and bound his head…
All:	With vinegar and brown paper.
Jill:	But you're not that Jack!
Jack:	I may have an identity crisis!
Assistant 1:	Use our bandages, they'll be excellent!
	(Suddenly the Assistants notice the cameras and start playing to them changing into the style of a demonstrator in an advertisement scene.)
Assistant 2:	They're the very best,
Assistant 1:	… complete with aromas from Ganderland Farm to distract you from your pain.
Assistant 2:	All these aromatic bandages are on a special
Assistants 1 & 2:	… "buy one get one free" offer…
Assistant 1:	… if you want bandages…
Assistants 1 & 2:	… look no further!
Jack:	You're profiting from other people's pain! Just take your counter *(Jack pushes the counter away and bundles the assistant off stage.)* and we'll go look for a fish and chip shop!
Jill:	That was a bit harsh!
Jack:	Don't you start!
Jill:	Jack?
Jack:	What?

Chapter 6

Jill:	We're arguing!
	(Add a subtitle to the screen – or a handheld sign - saying: JACK AND JILL'S FIRST ARGUMENT!)
Jack:	No we're not!
Jill:	Oh yes, we are… this is our…
Jack & Jill:	… first argument!
Jack:	And it's making my head hurt!
Jill:	To prove how much I love you Jack… I will find vinegar and brown paper if it's the last thing I do. *(She starts to search manically.)*
Jack:	My head hurts!
Becky:	*(Entering with vinegar and brown paper.)* Here you are love. Your head looks very sore.
Jack:	Wow! Now that was fast!
Jill:	Thanks Mum.
Becky:	I was watching it at home… very good… you're doing well… now, shall I wrap his head in it?
Jack:	Would you, Mrs Wentup. *(She does so, and Jill puts the crown on top to keep it in place)* Ah, that's better. Thanks!
Becky:	You're spending all this time with my daughter and I hardly know you. Do you want to come round to tea?
Jack:	Maybe tomorrow Mrs Wentup… I've got to go or I'll be late for Wolfey.
Becky:	Wolfey?
Jill:	Leave it Mum… it's all rumours! She was actually speared to death by a pack of Unicorns.
Becky:	I thought Unicorns were friendly.
Jack:	These were from the East side.

All:	*(With hand gesture)* East side!
Jack:	Right, I'm off then.
Jill:	Take care then.
Jack:	See you.
Jill:	Love you!
Jack:	Yeh. Me too!
Jack & Jill:	Bye. *(Jack exits.)*
Becky:	I hope he's not doing anything dodgy…
Jill:	Shame he's not this month's Reality Star, we could go home and watch where he goes!
Becky:	But… if something happened to Wolfey… then we could all find out…
Jill:	How?
Becky:	You could go with him.
Jill:	Yeh… IF something's happened to Wolfey… IF mum!
Jack:	*(Returning)* You're not gonna believe this?
Becky:	Something's happened to Wolfey?
Jack:	How do you know?
Jill:	Lucky guess… what's happened?
Jack:	He was in the forest and this little girl came and ate him up!
Jill:	Ate him?
Jack:	Yeh!
Jill:	She must've been really hungry!
Jack:	So… I need someone to accompany me on my mission!
Becky:	How about Jill?

Chapter 6

Music: Ironside *(Extract)* by Quincy Jones from the Kill Bill soundtrack.

(The cameras encircle Jill. They move away as the music fades.)

Jack: Jill?

Jill: Yeh. Why not?

Jack: What about them though? They follow you everywhere.

Jill: They never interfere… it's in the contract!

Becky: They've got no social conscience.

Jack, Jill & Becky: Someone'll have to die on one of their shows before that changes.

Music: Ironside *(Extract)* by Quincy Jones from the Kill Bill soundtrack.

(The cameras encircle Jill. They move away as the music fades.)

Jack: Yeh but…

Jill: Jack… I'll do anything for you… no matter what it is.

Jack: Mrs Wentup?

Becky: You will look after her, won't you?

Jack: Course I will.

Becky: What time'll you be back?

Jack: About ten… ok?

Becky: Thanks Jack. *(She exits.)*

Jill: So? Where're we going?

Jack: You are serious about coming with me…

Jill: Course I am!

Jack: You won't chicken out at the last minute?

Jill:	As if!
Jack:	*(Laughs)* I can't wait to show you!
Jill:	I can't wait to see! Come on then… what are we waiting for?
Jack:	The flipping scene to change to…
All:	The interior of a castle!
Jill:	Come on then you guys! Quick!
Jill & Jack:	We want adventure!

Chapter 7:   Inside the Castle!

Music: Woo Hoo by The 5,6,7, 8's from the Kill Bill Soundtrack. (As the music plays, the scene is changed to depict the interior of a fantasy castle. A bookshelf SL and a fireplace USC can be seen clearly. Jack and Jill are DSL. This could, alternatively, (perhaps) be achieved with body scenery (or, as in the original production) imaginative use of other objects – door frames were used in different ways throughout the play and in this scene were used together with a simple body-prop arrangement. A shaft of light sweeps in as though through a window from USR.)

Jack:	*(To a Camera Operator)* You're gonna love this!
Jill:	This is one cool place!
Jack:	I know.
Jill:	Ssssh!
Jack:	What?
Jill:	Thought I heard something.
Jack:	Doubt it.
Jill:	Listen.
	(Silence)
Jack:	I can't hear anything.
Jill:	Sorry. So, what happens now?
Jack:	You get yourself over there and…
Jill:	Me?
Jack:	Yeh.
Jill:	Why me?
Jack:	Well, I will if you want… it's just that… well, that's what Wolfey normally does… and me, I normally…
Jill:	It is safe?
Jack:	Course.

Jill:	What do I do?
Jack:	See that shelf…
Jill:	Yeh..
Jack:	Push the one at the bottom and the fireplace will turn… there's a space for me to go in.
Jill:	What?
Jack:	Look… *(Pointing)*…it's a secret door. *(If portrayed by a body prop, the secret door could wave enthusiastically for a moment.)*
Jill:	Wow!
Jack:	You stay still while I go in. It'll take me a minute or two to get it.
Jill:	What?
Jack:	There'll be an egg?
Jill:	An Egg?
Jack:	You'll see.
Jill:	I don't get it.
Jack:	You will. Trust me and once I'm out… push the shelf again and the door'll close.
Jill:	Then what?
Jack:	That's it.
Jill:	What?
Jack:	We get out!
Jill:	With an egg?
Jack:	It's not just any egg… it's… look… you're gonna have to just trust me.
Jill:	Why do we have to be so quiet if no-one lives here?
Jack:	I never said no-one lives here!

Chapter 7

Jill:	Did.
Jack:	I said I've never seen anyone… trust me… it's fine.
Jill:	I know, it's just…
Jack:	Ssssh. Don't even think about it.
Jill:	*(To camera)* I'm glad you're here… it makes me feel safer.
Jack:	Ready?
Jill:	Suppose.
Jack:	Go on then.
Jill:	Now?
Jack:	Quiet as you can…
Jill:	*(Creeping towards the shelf)* It doesn't feel…
Jack:	Just push the bloody shelf!
	Music: Battle Without Honour or Humanity by Tomoyasu Hotei from the Kill Bill soundtrack *underscores the following scene adding to the tension. She pushes it and the fireplace moves revealing an entrance. Jack creeps through it. As the music changes tempo, George enters USR. His shadow falls across the floor and shows clearly that he carries a gun. He does not move. Silence. Slowly George points the gun at Jill and fires. Jill screams and falls clutching her side. The music fades.*
Jill:	Aaargh! *(She manoeuvres herself slowly in the direction of an exit.)*
George:	One down. One to go.
Jill:	There's no one else. Just me!
George:	There were two what come in!
Jill:	I'm on my own. *(Getting out her mobile phone.)*
George:	I saw two!

Jill:	I'm bleeding, real bad! *(Looking at her mobile.)*
George:	I can see what you're doing… it won't help you. Phones are no use to anyone up here?
Jill:	What? No signal?
George:	Nope.
Jill:	What?
George:	No signals at the top of beanstalks… no coverage at all.
Jill:	How do you get ambulances up here?
George:	We don't.
Jill:	What if I die?
George:	I should get a bright shiny medal for doing it! A little scrote caught thievin'.
Jill:	You gotta get someone to help.
George:	*(Laughing.)* Why?
Jill:	You just shot me!
George:	*(Laughing.)* I don't have to do nothing missy. It's you what has to do sommut *(sic)*!
Jill:	What do you mean?
George:	Tell me who came in with you?
Jill:	I was on my own.
George:	Playing games are we?
Jill:	I'm really hurting!
George:	Why did you break in again after I warned you?
Jill:	You didn't warn me… you just shot!
George:	Last week I saw you both leaving… I shouted… don't pretend you didn't hear me!
Jill:	I've never been here before. Anyway we didn't

Chapter 7

	break in… we just…
George:	"We?" You said "we". So there is someone else? Tell 'em to come out or do I smoke 'em out?
Jill:	He didn't know anyone lived here.
George:	Someone's in my safe. You want me to shoot in there, do you?

(Silence)
(George shoots towards the fireplace.)

Jill:	Stop!
George:	When I were watchin' you climbing up this beanstalk I were sayin' to mysen *(sic)* "They'll pay for this, they will." I mean I warned you last time…
Jill:	But I've never been here before!
George:	And I warned the old Bill. I told 'em I'd take it into my own hands if they didn't do nuttin'. And that's what I done.
Jill:	I can't stop the bleeding. Please? Aren't you gonna help?
George:	Not till you play ball with me. Get your little friend to show his face… I have to say I didn't imagine you were a girl.
Jill:	That's sexist!
George:	Better than being a thief!
Jill:	If I get him out… will you let us go? Will you let us out of here?
George:	If you don't, you'll never find out, will you? I'll give him ten to come out by himself. One.
Jill:	Jack!
George:	Two.
Jack:	*(Off)* It's a trick.

George:	Three…
Jill:	He's serious!
George:	Four.
Jill:	*(To the area where Jack is.)* He's already taken a pop at me and I need help.
George:	Five.
Jill:	Jack! Quick!
George:	Six. *(He moves into the room and can for the first time be seen out of shadow and he can see a Camera Operator.)* What's going on? Who's he?
Jill:	It's for a TV programme.
George:	What?
Jill:	A Reality thing?
George:	Reality?
Jill:	It's hard to explain.
George:	Did they help you get in?
Jill:	Not exactly.
George:	But they let all this happen?
Jill:	Yeh, suppose.
George:	Why?
Jill:	Look, please, I'm… *(She looks down at her injuries.)* Look at the blood!
George:	They've filmed all this? *(Turning the gun towards a Camera Operator.)* Come on then mate… what's going on?
	(Silence.)
Jill:	They're not allowed to get involved.

Chapter 7

George:	They'd bloody well better... breaking into my castle like this... the least they can do is explain what they're up to... else they'll get a bullet, too! *(Aggressively pointing the gun at a Camera Operator. Shouting.)* Come on!
Jill:	Please! Let me out! *(To a Camera Operator.)* Get me an ambulance or something!
George:	She'll need an airlift... NHS won't run to that... they'll never believe you anyway... what you gonna say... we're on top of a beanstalk? *(Laughs.)*
Jill:	Please! One of you! You've got to do something! I think I'm dying!
Camera Operator:	*(Leaving his/her camera.)* No bloody producers are here... and it's nigh on impossible to get to the top of this beanstalk... I've got to do something!
Jill:	Get an ambulance!!! I'm bleeding to death here!
Camera Operator:	I'll do what I can... Jack get out here now... and go and get some help!
Jack:	No way!
George:	It's cos of what I said to the police, ain't it? That's why you lot're here. You've set me up. What did you think I'd do? I'm on my own here... make them a cup of tea? They could do ought to me. I mean... you don't naturally think you got friendly burglars do you? *(The Camera Operator should always, although confronting George, keep a distance from him viewing the gun as an opposing magnet. George should not move unless instructed and remain in a position where he can see everyone else at all times.)*
Camera Operator:	Can you put your gun down?
George:	No decent man should be put in the position where he can't defend himself.

Jill:	We didn't threaten you at all… *(A sudden surge of pain passes through her.)* Aaargh!
George:	I still don't know if the other one's got a gun!
Jill:	Well, he hasn't!
George:	He could have a nuke for all I know! *(Turning to Camera Operator)* They can't just break into my house and attack me, just cos they fancy it!
Jill:	We didn't attack anyone.
George:	You were about to…
Jill:	Wasn't!
Camera Operator:	Well, no one's threatening you now, so put your gun down.
George:	You're trespassing.
Camera Operator:	I'm making a TV programme. I haven't got a gun. I'm not here to rob you!
George:	But this is my castle!
Camera Operator:	I want you to put your gun down, Mr Jhiyonne.
George:	Not until you get off my property.
Camera Operator:	Everyone saw you ambush her like a rat in a trap. You gave her no warning… nothing! You were waiting for her then you shot at her. I hope you get a good solicitor. *(Quietly, almost unobserved, Jill falls into unconsciousness. Neither George nor the Camera Operator notice what has happened. If there are other Camera Operators, they can notice her and move in for a close up. If the resultant camera work is being aired on a screen it is this shot that should be chosen.)*
George:	I don't need a bloody solicitor.
	No solicitor will go along with capital punishment for burglars.

George:	But I ain't done nothing wrong. I was defending mysen. There was two of them and one of me. I did what anyone else would have done! It's you who needs the bloody solicitor.
Camera Operator:	*(Going to Jill.)* Jill, are you ok? I think we're losing her. Do something someone… get some bloody help! *(Rushing over to her.)* Someone'll be here soon… it's going out live.
George:	Live?
Camera Operator:	This ain't gonna look good for you if she dies in your castle!
George:	You've stitched me up.
Camera Operator:	We haven't done anything!
George:	I was scared they'd attack me!
Camera Operator:	You weren't!
George:	Was.
Camera Operator:	No! You were angry!
George:	You've set me up… trapped me… ambushed me… that's the word. You ambushed me and made it look like I'm in the wrong! This is my castle! If you were in my shoes you would've done the same!
Camera Operator:	So what are you gonna do then… shoot me too just to shut me up?
George:	You've bloody destroyed me. The world's gone mad. *(George slowly turns the gun on himself.)*
Camera Operator:	No!
George:	I don't know what to think any more.
Camera Operator:	George… this won't help!
George:	You… you keep your wicked little lives,
Camera Operator:	Stop please!

George:	I don't want mine anymore.
Camera Operator:	George! *(George shoots himself and falls to the floor, dead.)*
Jack:	*(Emerges, peeping his head out.)* What the hell's…?
Camera Operator:	Jack.
Jack:	Has she…? *(He runs over to Jill's corpse.)* Oh… what have I done?
Camera Operator:	It wasn't you.
Jack:	Yeh but…
Camera Operator:	He was mad…
Jack:	Yeh, but I bought her here… it's all my fault! She was my first girlfriend… I really loved her… I didn't think he'd shot her… not to kill like. *(Addressing Jill)* I didn't mean it to be like this… Jill I'm sorry… I'm really sorry.
Camera Operator:	You loved her, didn't you?
Jack:	We had plans. What am I gonna do now?
Voice Over:	We're flying the girl's mother in… she's coming in now! You're part of television history here!
Jack:	What?
Voice Over:	She's coming in now! This will be television history!
Camera Operator:	Who gives a shit about television history… you could have flown in paramedics in earlier!
Voice Over:	That wouldn't have been reality… it would have been us…
CO & VO:	… changing the course of history…
Camera Operator:	I know, I know… but this isn't right… it can't be!
Voice Over:	You committed the cardinal sin… allowing yourself to see them as real…

Chapter 7

Camera Operator:	They are!
Jack:	I am real! This was my life!
Voice Over:	It a reality **show!**
Camera Operator:	And here comes the next installment, eh?
Voice Over:	You said it! Stand back and allow history to happen.
Becky:	*(Entering)* Jack? What have you done?
Jack:	I'm sorry.
Becky:	*(She runs over to Jill and cradles her.)* You promised you'd look after her!
Jack:	I can't take this!
Becky:	And I can?
Jack:	I'm off!
Becky:	To where Jack? You're at the top of a bloody beanstalk!
Jack:	Who cares? I'll jump!
Becky:	*(Grabbing hold of Jack tight.)* Jack… No way!
Jack:	I didn't know he was in. I'm so sorry! Look… I've got to go! *(He goes to leave.)*
Becky:	Face it… and me… and what's happened to Jill.
Jack:	Let go of me!
Becky:	No Jack! You're all the same you men… running away from your problems… first her dad…
Jack:	*(Shouting)* Let go!
Becky:	… then her killer… but not her first boyfriend! Please. Stay Jack.
Jack:	*(Shouting and pushing her away)* Let go of me! *(As she is forced away Jack crumples)* I so loved her… but we couldn't … because of the cameras… we were going to… I was so… honest

	I really loved her… and I'm… I don't know what to say! *(He breaks down.)*
Becky:	*(To Camera Operator)* How can you lot do this to people?
Voice Over:	You can't blame us for what Jill did….
Camera Operator:	This'll go to Court… *(To VO)*… then you'll have to face up to your responsibility.
Voice Over:	We can't be responsible for their actions.
Becky:	Jill!
Camera Operator:	They'll decide on the evidence.
Becky:	Jill come back to me!
Voice Over:	Exactly… evidence not emotions… that's how courts work.
Becky:	Please! Isn't there something someone can do?
Camera Operator:	What do you mean?
Voice Over:	Courts don't decide cases on sympathy.
Becky:	My daughter… my beautiful daughter.
Camera Operator:	All of us will be judged. *(Scared)* And it'll be shown on TV.
Voice Over:	As I say… television history in the making!
Becky:	Killed in the name of entertainment. How's this been allowed to happen?
All:	*(There is the overpowering sound of an axe or chain-saw chopping loudly.)* What on earth's that?
Camera Operator:	I wish I hadn't ever got into this!
Voice Over:	There's no escape for any of you now…
Becky:	Don't you care what's happened?
Camera Operator:	How are they going to get us down?

Chapter 7

Jack:	Are you thinking what I'm thinking?
All:	They're chopping it down…
Camera Operator:	Who?
Voice Over:	It's just the public having their say.
Camera Operator:	You can't have trial by television… everyone knows that!
Voice Over:	Get used to it!
Camera Operator:	They're chopping us down… what about you?
Voice Over:	The public have decided!
Jack:	I'm sorry Mrs Wentup… I am… I'm so sorry!
Becky:	But when people remember Jill… *(Referring to George)*… they'll remember him too… I don't want them remembered together… that's not right… I don't want it to be like that…
Voice Over:	Cut transmission.
	(Blackout. The sound of the beanstalk tumbling to the ground accompanied by all the humans shouting.)
All:	Aaaaaaargh!
Voice Over:	Now gently fade up the music and cameras… action… let's have a really tight focus on Jill and George…
	Music: Bang Bang (My Baby Shot Me Down) by Nancy Sinatra *from the Kill Bill soundtrack.*
	Excellent… excellent!
	(The corpses of George and Jill are left together on stage framed by a spotlight as the music – above – plays.)

Chapter 6a: Jack's Back Story (Deleted Scene... the original...)

	(Jack and Jill are on stage. The storytellers run on and surround them.)
Jill & Jack:	Who the hell are you?
Storytellers:	Storytellers... and very cheap!
Jill & Jack:	We have to pay?
Storytellers:	Two-thousand and fifty quanders.
Jill & Jack:	Call that cheap?
Storytellers:	Ha ha! We were joking... one and a half quanders.
Jill:	And what do we get for that?
Storytellers:	A story?
Jill & Jack:	What kind of story?
Storytellers:	Jack's Flashback story... from Flashback City!
Jill & Jack:	Flashback City?
Storytellers:	The city where every flashback is logged and preserved!
Jill & Jack:	Alright... but be quick... we've things to do...
Jill:	People to see...
Jill & Jack:	An adventure to be... advented!
Storytellers:	Sit back and relax...
S 1:	Once there was a boy called Jack. *(S 1 becomes Jack)* Searching in his kitchen for something to eat.
Jack:	That's me! *(Some Storytellers become units in Jack's kitchen. Jack opens cupboard doors and, as he does, each one says:)*
Storytellers:	No more food, ha ha ha!!! *(This builds to a climax as the cupboards move threateningly towards Jack and surround Jack.)*
S 1:	Mum?

Chapter 6a

S 2:	*(Off)* What?
S 1:	The cupboards are talking!
S 2:	*(Off)* Don't be a dipstick!
S 1:	And moving! *(The cupboards dart back to their original positions making faces at Jack as they do.)* Maybe I'm just hallucinating cos I'm so flipping hungry! *(S 2 enters as Jack's mum.)* Mum, I need breakfast!
S 2:	Jack, we've only one thing left that's edible… Buttercup !
S 1:	No! No, I could never eat Buttercup!
S 2:	Then you must take her to market and… sell her!
S 1:	And what Mum?
S 2:	And sell her!
S 1:	Sell Buttercup? *(He begins to cry.)*
Jack:	That's just how it was …
Jill:	Sssh Jack! Let 'em get on with it.
S 1:	*(As the following line is said, the kitchen units elegantly morph into the barn. S 3 becomes Buttercup now in the newly constructed barn.)*
S 1:	*(Desperate.)* "You can't mum… you can't!" But the next moment… *(Jack approaches Buttercup .)*
Jack:	I was well upset… crying! Real tears they were!
Jill:	*(Hugging him fondly.)* You're so different to all the other guys!
S 1:	Buttercup … I'm so sorry… but… well if I don't… we can't eat… so… you've got to understand?
S 3:	Mooo.
S 1:	I'm so sorry.
S 3:	Mooo!

S 1:	Moments later Buttercup and Jack were in the market square *(The barn becomes market traders etc. Jack is walking with Buttercup – two of the other storytellers)...*
S 4:	... when a strange young woman approached them. "Come hence young boy... *(Jack moves away out of her path)...* hither!"
S 1:	Me?
S 4:	By my troth there is none other.
S 1:	What?
S 4:	Pray you now. Thy cow? Wilt thou trade?
S 3:	Mooo!
S 4:	As here have I beans... beans to make thy days more contented.
S 1:	I need quanders... not crappy beans... out of my way you ugly old hag!
S 4:	You do me wrong.
S 1:	I'm not swapping my precious Buttercup!
S 3:	Mooo!
S 1:	... for a few stupid beans!
S 4:	*(Becoming aggressive.)* Be ye not so hasty young sir. I can offer this beast a life of plenty.
S 3:	Mooo!
S 4:	Nature will smile on her every need in her twilight years
S 3:	Mooo!!! *(Buttercup's tail begins to wag.)*
S 4:	If thou care'st for her... thou shalt do this. How now?
S 1:	I'm not sure.
S 3:	Moo! Moo-yakasha!

	(With a commanding sense of performance!) Respec' Jack! Trade wid da beans! My special cow powers inform dat dey is bangin' innit! You can still visit I in me sick crib? I hates dat shit barn you've leave I in... not that I is moanin', innit! Moohyakasha!
Jill & Jack:	Quality performance man!
S 3:	Thanks mate!
S 1:	What if these beans aren't magic?
S 4:	Thy sacred beast I shall return unto you.
S 1:	My mum'll go ape!
S 4:	On the rising of the sun thy mother's smile will sing in the air.
S 1:	And with that, the deal was sealed and Jack kissed Buttercup a fond farewell *(S3 & 4 exit)* and made his way home, imagining as he walked, how his dear mother may react:
All:	Scenario 1...
S 2:	How did you get on Jack?
S 1:	Mum... you'd better sit down...
S 2:	What's happened? Buttercup didn't die on the way, did she?
S 1:	No... promise you're not going to shout?
S 2:	Tell me what's happened?
S 1:	I swapped Buttercup for some magic beans.
S 2:	Magic beans?
S 1:	They're guaranteed.
S 2:	Are they?
S 1:	Yeh... look... when I throw them into the garden... *(He opens the window and hurls the beans out into the garden)*... magic things will happen!

	(Silence)
S 2:	Like what?
S 1:	I don't know exactly… but they will! They're guaranteed.
S 1 & 2:	Look! Magic things are happening!
S 4:	Ting! *(S4 plays the beanstalk who, when fully grown, says the aforementioned word!)*
Jack:	Er no! It wasn't like that! I went home and… I remember it like it was yesterday.
S 2:	*(Bellowing)* You swapped our beloved Buttercup for some so called magic beans from a woman who hadn't even got a market stall! You're an idiot Jack… a waste of space… and so are these beans!
	Music: Ironside *(Extract)* **by Quincy Jones from the Kill Bill soundtrack.** *(She opens the window and draws back her hand to throw the beans. In slow motion she hurls them out of the window.)*
S 1:	*(Also in slow motion.)* No Mum… No! Don't! They're magic! *(S 4 again grows into a beanstalk and says:)*
S4:	Ting!
Jill:	Wow! What happened then?
Jack:	You'll find out… if you're serious about coming with me…
Jill:	Course I am!
Jack:	You won't chicken out at the last minute?
Jill:	As if!
Jack:	*(Laughs.)* I can't wait to show you!
Jill:	I can't wait to see! Come on then… what are we waiting for?

Chapter 6a

Jack:	The flipping scene to change…
Jill:	Come on then you guys! Quick!
Jill & Jack:	We want adventure!

If you have enjoyed reading and/or working with this playscript, you may like to find out about other plays we publish. There are brief descriptions and other details on the following pages.

All plays deal with contemporary social and moral issues and are suitable for Youth Theatres, Schools, Colleges, and adult AmDram. They are ideal for GCSE Drama/English exam use and frequently do well in One Act Play Festivals. They offer both male and female performers equally challenging opportunities.

For enquiries or to order plays published by *dbda*, please contact:
dbda, Pin Point, Rosslyn Crescent, Harrow HA1 2SB.
Tel: 0870 333 7771
Email: info@dbda.co.uk

All enquiries regarding performing rights of plays by
Mark Wheeller*, *Danny Sturrock* and *Johnny Carrington
should be made to:
Sophie Gorell Barnes, MBA Literary Agents,
62 Grafton Way, London W1P 5LD.
Tel: 020 7387 2076
E-mail: sophie@mbalit.co.uk

All enquiries regarding performing rights of 'Heroin Lies' by
***Wayne Denfhy*, should be made to:**
Wayne Denfhy, c/o ***dbda***,
Pin Point, Rosslyn Crescent, Harrow HA1 2SB.
Tel: 0870 333 7771
Email: info@dbda.co.uk (subject: Wayne Denfhy)

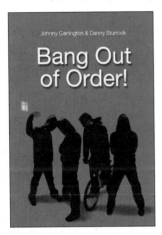

Johnny Carrington & Danny Sturrock

Bang Out of Order!

ISBN 9 781902 843216

Cast: 2m & 2f
Suitable for GCSE
Duration: 55 minutes *approx.*
KS 3 & 4

Supported by Southampton City Council, the play was awarded a Home Office 'Taking A Stand' award in April 2006.

Written by two new writers, this is a first play for Johnny Carrington and the second one for Danny Sturrock after his highly acclaimed debut play 'Gagging For It'.

NEW! - BANG OUT OF ORDER
by Johnny Carrington & Danny Sturrock

4 friends, 1 secret, 1 chance, 1 life. Written by Johnny Carrington & Danny Sturrock, the play tackles anti-social behaviour head on. This rollercoaster ride will educate, amuse and challenge.

Set on an urban estate in the UK, newcomer Ollie has a history of antisocial behaviour and is attempting to reform. His family are forced to move away in an attempt to make a fresh start… but once he is accepted into the local group of youths, things start to go wrong.

The play tackles the issues of anti-social behaviour using a mixture of comedy, dance, music and multi-media.

'If you are setting out to convey a message, the mixture of naturalism which pulls no punches, stylised movement that moves the action along with wit and mixed media, adds another dimension that certainly grabs the attention of the audience.'

Fran Morley, Youth & Community Director,
Nuffield Theatre Southampton

'It was a really exciting and unpredictable production. I felt the audience's hearts collectively dropped as they watched the young friends' lives plunged back into the turmoil of their inner-city lives. There can't be many productions that present hard-edged in your face aggression, then disarm you with humour and tenderness.'

Paul Mills, Head of Drama
Westgate School, Winchester

Other plays published by *dbda*

ISBN 1 902843 17 1

Cast: 3f, 3m &3m/f or 3m & 3f
for GCSE using suggested cuts
Duration: 55 minutes approx.
KS 3 & 4.

Gagging for it by Danny Sturrock

Summer is here, A-levels are over and a group of 6 friends embark on a holiday to Ibiza! What would their holiday bring? Would Chris finally pluck up the courage to ask out Teresa? Would Jay drink himself into oblivion? Would Bianca spend the entire holiday flirting with the Spanish barmen – more than likely! ...or would their experiments with drugs bring their hedonistic worlds crashing down around them!?

Comedy, dance music and choreography are the keys to this production. The pace is breakneck and hilarious, but once the party's over, it hits you!

'Really funny... laugh out loud funny. Inspired outstanding performances from the six Year 11s who went on to exceed our expectations by a long way in their GCSEs achieving A or A*. It proved to be a firm favourite with our KS3/4 audience.'

Mark Wheeller

ISBN 1 902843 18 5

Cast: 2f & 2m with doubling
Duration: 60 minutes approx.
KS 3 & 4 and A Level

Legal Weapon II by Mark Wheeller

This is a new "improved" version of the popular *Legal Weapon* play which is touring schools across the UK.

It is the story of a young man, Andy. His relationship with his girlfriend – and his car – are both flawed, but his speeding causes the loss of a life and the loss of his freedom.

In *Legal Weapon II*, the story takes an additional twist when Andy realises that the person he's killed is somebody very dear to Jazz, his girlfriend.

Legal Weapon II promises to be faster, funnier and far more powerful!

'A gripping storyline. Even the most challenging of our students were held by the drama. This learning experience should be given to each Year 11 as they come through the school.'

Myrtle Springs Secondary School

Other plays published by *dbda*

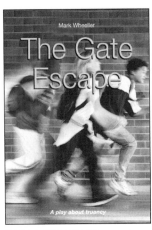

ISBN 1 902843 14 2

Cast: 2f & 2m with doubling, or up to 30
Duration: 70 minutes
KS 3&4

The Gate Escape by Mark Wheeller

The story of two truants. Corey is 'addicted' to bunking school. Chalkie views himself as a casual truant "no problem!" While truanting with some friends, the pair are greeted by a surreal 'Big Brother' figure who sets them a task. The loser will be in for some dramatic 'Big Bother'... Who will lose?... What will this 'bother' be?

The play has toured professionally throughout the south of England to great acclaim.

'A lively dramatic style and innovative structure with dynamic and contemporary dialogue. It is written in a way to guarantee that the audience will feel fully involved and enthralled by the main characters.'

Professor Ken Reid, Author of Tackling Truancy in Schools

'Theatrically interesting... excellent basis for active discussion of issues and dramatic style with reluctant GCSE students' Ali Warren (National Drama)

ISBN 1 902843 15 0

Cast: 8f, 7m and 2m/f
Duration: 70 minutes approx.
KS 3&4

Heroin Lies by Wayne Denfhy

A sensitive, yet disturbing look at drugs and drug dependency, in particular the pressures and influences at play on an ordinary teenage girl. We observe Vicki's gradual and tragic slide towards addiction and also the various degrees of help and hindrance she receives from family and friends.

This is a new, updated edition of Wayne Denfhy's popular play. It is suitable for performance as well as for reading in the class. Included with the playscript is an excellent scheme for follow-up work by Peter Rowlands.

'...a piece of drama that will stimulate and challenge a young cast... Heroin Lies deals with vital issues that affect today's youngsters in a gentle and humane way and, in so doing, gets its message across without the instant rejection that can meet other approaches.'

Pete Sanpher, Head of Drama, Norfolk

Other plays published by *dbda*

CHICKEN! by Mark Wheeller
New Updated Edition

A 'new and improved' version of WHY DID THE CHICKEN CROSS THE ROAD? The play tells the story of two cousins, Tammy and Chris. We are led to believe that something bad will happen to Chris who refuses to wear his cycle helmet. It is, however, Tammy who gets killed on the one morning that the cousins walk to school. Chris remains unwilling to tell anyone of his part in the accident and he has to live with this dreadful secret. One of the main changes is the introduction of Chris filming Tammy's fatal dare on his mobile phone camera.

ISBN 1 902843 19 3

Cast: 4m, 3f & 2m/f or 2m & 2f for GCSE
Duration: 35 minutes
KS 3 & 4

'We have just been fortunate enough to witness the most superb exhibition of interactive safety education. The performance was quite stunning!'

Jim Lambert, Head Teacher Sinclair Middle School, Southampton

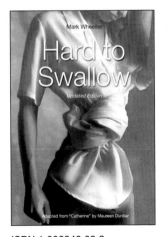

Hard to Swallow by Mark Wheeller

This play is an adaptation of Maureen Dunbar's award winning book (and film) *Catherine* which charts her daughter's uneven battle with anorexia and the family's difficulties in coping with the illness.

The play has gone on to be performed all over the world to much acclaim, achieving considerable success in One Act Play Festivals. Its simple narrative style means that it is equally suitable for adult and older youth groups to perform.

'This play reaches moments of almost unbearable intensity... naturalistic scenes flow seamlessly into sequences of highly stylised theatre... such potent theatre!'

Vera Lustiq, The Independent

'Uncompromising and sensitive... should be compulsory viewing to anyone connected with the education of teenagers.'

Mick Martin, Times Educational Supplement

ISBN 1 902843 08 8

Cast: 3f & 2m with doubling, or 6f, 3m & 16
Duration: 70 minutes
KS 3 to adult

Other plays published by *dbda*

GRAHAM – World's Fastest Blind Man!
by Mark Wheeller

A play full of lively humour telling the inspirational story of Graham Salmon MBE. Totally blind since birth, Graham went on to become the World's Fastest Blind Man running 100 metres in 11.4 seconds!

The play, written in Mark's unique documentary style, skillfully brings to life Graham's courage, tenacity and wonderful sense of humour.

'GRAHAM was an ideal piece to challenge my group; it ticked all the boxes for A Level work. My Year 12 students who performed it as part of their AS Level did exceptionally well. All seven of them not only got the top grade for the performance but they were all awarded 120/120 marks!'

Mike Fleetwood, Parkside Arts College

ISBN 1 902843 09 6

Cast: 5m & 4f with doubling, or up to 34
Duration: 80 minutes approx.
KS 3/4 to adult

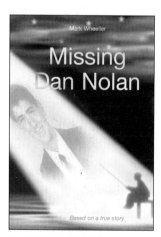

Missing Dan Nolan (based on a true story)
by Mark Wheeller

This play, based on the true story of Dan Nolan, a teenage boy who went missing on the night of January 1st 2002, is written in the same documentary style as *Too Much Punch for Judy*. It has won awards and commendations at every Drama Festival it has entered. It is now, like so many of Mark's other plays, being toured professionally by the Queens Theatre in Hornchurch, Essex.

'Unusual and deeply affecting. Skillfully written... achieves astonishing depth and authenticity... '

Charles Evans, Adjudicator, Eastleigh Drama Festival

'I feel very proud. All the issues about our Dan's disappearance, and the safety issues surrounding teenagers, are in the play and it will continue to raise awareness'

Pauline Nolan (Dan's mother)

ISBN 1 902843 16 9

Cast: 2m & 2f with doubling, or up to 18
Duration: 45-50 minutes
KS 3/4 to adult

Other plays published by *dbda*

WACKY SOAP by Mark Wheeller

Wacky Soap is a Pythonesque allegorical tale about 'substance' abuse (drugs, alcohol, glue, tobacco, etc). While washing with Wacky Soap leads to instant happiness and an inclination towards outrageous behaviour, prolonged use washes away limbs and ultimately leads to dematerialisation. This has become a tried and tested (and increasingly popular) School/ Drama Club/ Youth Theatre production and is an ideal vehicle for a cast of any age.

'Wacky Soap is a brilliant show for any age group. It has the "Wow factor" not the "Yawn factor" so often associated with educational material. The script is fast and comical. The songs are wonderfully catchy. The Audience at the end were calling for more'.

Sally Dwyer, Hants Drama Teacher/
Eastleigh Borough Youth Theatre Director

ISBN 1 902843 02 9

The full version of the Musical play which includes scheme of work for KS3/4.

The story of Wacky Soap first appeared as a full **Musical play**. A mini version of the play is included with the **Music Score**. The **Storybook**, as well as being a wonderful book to read on its own, is often used for inspiration with props and costumes for the play. A **Past-performance CD** gives you the opportunity to hear the songs of the play, while a fully orchestrated **Backing track CD** will be invaluable to those who want to produce the play but do not have music facilities.

ISBN 1 902843 07 X

A fully illustrated book with the story of Wacky Soap in narrative form.

ISBN 1 902843 06 1

*A companion book with the Music Score and a **Mini-Musical** version of the play.*

Past Performance and Backing track CDs

63

Other Plays by Mark Wheeller (not published by *dbda*)

Sequinned Suits And Platform Boots
Duration: 55 mins   **Cast:** 6f, 7m & 1m or f
Published by: Maverick Musicals: http://www.mavmuse.com/default.asp
A play that seems more like a Musical! Sequinned Suits and Platform Boots is Mark Wheeller's new One Act comedy tribute to the colourful Glam Rock years. It charts (semi-autobiographically) the teenage years of Shakey Threwer and his desperate attempt to be noticed by the Music industry. "Funky & funny... but be warned, it will have you coming away cringing at your own memories of singing into a hairbrush whilst staring at your reflection in the mirror." *Craig Morrison Southampton Institute Newspaper 2005*

Arson About   Script: Mark Wheeller (Ed. Andy Kempe)
Duration: 75 mins   **Cast:** 4 (2f & 2m with doubling)
Published by: Nelson Thornes Ltd. Tel: 01242 267100
Mollie and Ian are hot for each other. Stueey can be a real bright spark. Mr Butcher's comments have inflamed Shuttle. All in all it's combustible material but when you play with fire it can be more than your fingers that get burnt. Arson About is a theatrical power keg which crackles with wit and moves along with a scorching pace. But in this play by Mark Wheeller the cost of 'arson about' becomes all too clear.

Chunnel of Love   Script: Graham Cole & Mark Wheeller
Duration: 100 mins   **Cast:** 25 (11f, 8m & 6m/f)
Published by: Zig Zag Education. Tel: 0117 950 3199
A bi-lingual play (80% English & 20% French) about teenage pregnancy. Lucy is fourteen - she hopes to become a vet and is working hard to gain good grades in her GCSE exams, when she discovers she is pregnant. She faces a series of major decisions, not least of which is what to tell the father... Ideal as a school production and Key Stage 4 Drama course book.

Sweet FA !   Script: Mark Wheeller
Duration: 45 mins plus interval   **Cast:** 3f / 2m (or more)
Published by: SchoolPlay Productions Ltd. Tel: 01206 540111
A Zigger Zagger for girls (and boys)! A new play (also available as a full length Musical) telling the true life story of Southampton girl footballer Sarah Stanbury (Sedge) whose ambition is to play Football (Soccer) for England. Her dad is delighted... her mum disapproves strongly! An ideal GCSE production and Key Stage 4 Drama course book. Drama GCSE scheme of work also available.

Blackout – One Evacuee in Thousands   MUSICAL
Script: Mark Wheeller with the Stantonbury Youth Theatre   **Music:** Mark Wheeller
Duration: 90 mins plus interval   **Published by:** SchoolPlay Productions Ltd.
A Musical about the plight of Rachael Eagle, a fictional evacuee in World War II. Rachel's parents are determined that the war will not split the family up. After refusing to have her evacuated in 1939 they decide to do so midway though 1940. At first Rachael does not settle but, after the death of her mother, she becomes increasingly at home with her billets in Northamptonshire. When her father requests that she return she wants to stay where she feels at home. An ideal large scale school production with good parts for girls (and boys).

For more details and an up-to-date list of plays, please visit Mark's website:
www.amdram.co.uk/wheellerplays (*please note wheeller has two "l"*)